Winnie-the-Pooh's

Little

Frier

C000001253

Inspired by A.A. Milne & illustrated by E.H. Shepard

First published in Great Britain 2002
by Egmont Books Limited
239 Kensington High Street, London W8 6SA
Copyright © 2002 Michael John Brown, Peter Janson-Smith,
Roger High Vaughan Charles Morgan and Timothy Michael
Robinson, Trustees of the Pooh Properties
Selected from *Winnie-the-Pooh* and *The House at Pooh Corner*
and *Now We are Six*
Text by A. A. Milne and line illustrations by E. H. Shepard
Copyright under the Berne Convention
Book design © 2002 Egmont Books Limited

1 3 5 7 9 10 8 6 4 2

ISBN 1 4052 0066 9

Printed in Hong Kong

'Oh Pooh!' cried Christopher Robin,
'Where *are* you?'
'Here I am,' said a growly voice behind him.
'Pooh!'
They rushed into each others arms.

Winnie-the-Pooh's First Words

'What about me?' said Pooh sadly.
I suppose *I* shan't be useful?'

But of course without Pooh this little collection
of wise words about Friendship would have been
impossible, just like the adventures of Pooh
and his friends. And as Pooh says, it isn't much
good having adventures if you can't share them
with somebody special.

A True Friend is the Best Possession

Piglet sidled up to Pooh from behind.
'Pooh!' he whispered.
'Yes, Piglet?'
'Nothing,' said Piglet, taking Pooh's paw.
'I just wanted to be sure of you.'

Sharing is Important

And then Piglet gave a very long sigh and said,
'I wish Pooh were here. It's so much
more friendly with two.'

Choose your Friends Carefully

'I *like* talking to Rabbit. He talks about sensible things. He doesn't use long, difficult words, like Owl. He uses short, easy words, like "What about lunch?" and "Help yourself, Pooh."'

Share your Feelings

'It's bad enough,' said Eeyore, almost breaking
down, 'being miserable by myself, what with no
presents and no cake and no candles, and
no proper notice taken of me at all, but if
everybody else is going to be miserable too—'

It's Better to Give than to Receive…

Pooh hurried back home as quick as
he could; for he felt that he must get poor
Eeyore a present of *some* sort at once, and he
could always think of a proper one afterwards.

...but Receiving is Nice, Too

'Oh!' said Pooh.
'Oh, Pooh!' said everybody else
except Eeyore.
'Thank-you,' growled Pooh.

Don't Outstay your Welcome

'I was just beginning to think,' said Bear,
sniffing slightly, 'that Rabbit might never
be able to use his front door again.
And I should *hate* that,' he said.
'So should I,' said Rabbit.

Keep in Touch

Winnie-the-Pooh went round to his friend
Christopher Robin, who lived behind a
green door in another part of the Forest.
'Good morning, Christopher Robin,' he said.

Conversational Skills No. I

'"*Hallo — What*" — I mean, it gets you nowhere,
particularly if the other person's tail
is only just in sight for the
second half of the conversation.'

Credit where Credit's Due

'That, Piglet, is a *very* good idea. It is just
what Eeyore wants to cheer him up.
Nobody can be uncheered with a balloon.'
So off Piglet trotted…

It's the Thought that Counts

So Owl wrote…
and this is what he wrote:
HIPY PAPY BTHUTHDTH
THUTHDA BTHUTHDY.
Pooh looked on admiringly.

Have Time for Others

'And how are you?' said Winnie-the-Pooh.
'Not very how,' said Eeyore. 'I don't seem to
have felt at all how for a long time.'
'Dear, dear,' said Pooh, 'I'm sorry about that.
Let's have a look at you.'

Very Friendly

'You'll like Owl. He flew past a day or two ago and noticed me. He didn't actually say anything, mind you, but he knew it was me. Very friendly of him, I thought. Encouraging.'

Make Yourself Useful

'I say, old fellow,' said Rabbit, '*do* you mind
if I use your back legs as a towel-horse?
Because, I mean, there they are – doing nothing
– and it would be very convenient just to
hang the towels on them.'

Be Ready to Listen

'Would you read a Sustaining Book,
such as would help and comfort a
Wedged Bear in Great Tightness?'
So for a week Christopher Robin read that
sort of book at the North End of Pooh.

On Being Polite

'Pooh,' said Piglet reproachfully, 'haven't you
been listening to what Rabbit was saying?'
'I listened,' said Pooh, 'but I had a small
piece of fluff in my ear.
Could you say it again, please, Rabbit?'

You Scratch My Back…

Pooh sat down, dug his feet into the ground,
and pushed hard against Christopher Robin's
back, and Christopher Robin pushed hard
against his, and pulled and pulled at his
boot until he had got it on.

Know Your Friends

'Eeyore,' he said solemnly,
'I, Winnie-the-Pooh, will find
your tail for you.'
'Thank you, Pooh,' answered Eeyore.
'You're a real friend,' said he.

Value Friendship

It would have been jolly to talk…
and really, it wasn't much good having
anything exciting like floods, if you couldn't
share them with somebody.

Hospitality

'When you've been walking in the wind for miles, and you suddenly go into somebody's house, and he says, "Hallo, Pooh, you're just in time for a little smackerel of something," and you are, then it's what I call a Friendly Day.'

Recognise Strengths in Others

'If anyone knows anything about anything,'
said Bear to himself, 'it's Owl who knows
something about something,' he said, 'or my
name's not Winnie-the-Pooh,' he said.
'Which it is,' he added. 'So there you are.'

Pop in Unexpectedly

'Is anybody home?' called out Pooh very loudly.
'No!' said a voice...
'Bother!' said Pooh. 'Isn't there
anybody here at all?'
'Nobody.'

Be Prepared to Make
New Friends

... and Pooh wondering what a Grandfather was
like, and if perhaps this was Two Grandfathers
they were after now, and, if so, whether he would
be allowed to take one home and keep it...

Look After your Friends No. 1

Piglet took Pooh's arm,
in case Pooh was frightened.
'Is it One of the Fiercer Animals?' he said,
looking the other way.

Small Talk

They began to talk in a friendly way about
this and that, and Piglet said, 'If you see what
I mean, Pooh,' and Pooh said, 'It's just what I
think myself, Piglet,' and Piglet said, 'But on the
other hand, Pooh, we must remember...'

Look After your Friends No. 2

'Hallo, Pooh,' said Owl. 'How's things?'
'Terrible and Sad,' said Pooh, 'because Eeyore,
who is a friend of mine, has lost his tail.
And he's Moping about it. So could you
very kindly tell me how to find it for him?'

Kindness is the Very Stuff of Love

Kanga said very kindly, 'Well, look in my
cupboard, Tigger dear, and see what you'd like.'
Because she knew at once that, however
big Tigger seemed to be, he wanted as
much kindness as Roo.

Sarcasm isn't Friendly...

'Hello, Rabbit,' he said, 'is that you?'
'Let's pretend it isn't,' said Rabbit,
'and see what happens.'

... but Compliments are
Always Welcome

'You're the Best Bear in All the World,'
said Christopher Robin soothingly.
'Am I?' said Pooh hopefully.

Conversational Skills No. 2

'Hallo!' said Pooh.
'Hallo!' said Whatever-it-was.
'Oh!' said Pooh, 'Hallo!' 'Hallo!'
'Oh, *there* you are!' said Pooh. 'Hallo!'
'Hallo,' said the Strange Animal.

A Friend in Need

'Help, help!' cried Piglet,
'a Heffalump, a Horrible Heffalump!'
'Well,' said Christopher Robin, 'I shall go and
look at it. Come on.' Piglet wasn't afraid if he had
Christopher Robin with him, so off they went.

Be Sociable

'Aha!' said Pooh. 'If I know anything about anything that hole means Rabbit… and Rabbit means Company… and Company means Food and Listening-to-me-Humming and such like. Rum-tum-tum-tiddle-um.'

Pen-pals?

Some Friends Need *Several* Friends Indeed!

'Ow!' he shouted as the tree flew past him.
'Look out!' cried Christopher Robin to the
others. There was a crash, a tearing noise, and a
confused heap of everybody on the ground.

Best Friends

Pooh thought that being with Christopher
Robin was a very good thing to do, and having
Piglet near was a very friendly thing to have...
'I like that, too,' said Christopher Robin.

Happiness is for Sharing

When Christopher Robin had nailed it on in
its right place again, Eeyore frisked about the
Forest, waving his tail so happily that
Winnie-the-Pooh came over all funny...

Friends are People who'll Miss You

'Mind you don't get blown away, little Piglet.
You'd be missed. People would say
"Where's little Piglet been blown to?" –
really wanting to know...'

Quite Right, Eeyore

'A little Consideration, a little Thought
for Others, makes all the difference.'

Friends Pop Up in Unexpected Places

Pooh looked up at the sky, and then, as he heard
the whistle again, looked up into the branches of
a big oak tree, and then he saw a friend of his.
'It's Christopher Robin,' he said.

Honesty is Best

'Yes,' said Winnie-the-Pooh.
'I see now,' said Winnie-the-Pooh.
'I have been Foolish and Deluded,' said he,
'and I am a Bear of No Brain at All.'

Sharing Secrets

Pooh looked around to see that nobody else
was listening, and said in a very solemn voice.
'Piglet, I have decided something.'
'What have you decided, Pooh?'
'I have decided to catch a Heffalump.'

Listen...

For some time now Pooh had been saying
'Yes' and 'No' in turn, with his eyes shut, to all
that Owl was saying, and having said, 'Yes, yes,'
last time, he said, 'No, not at all,' now, without
really knowing what Owl was talking about.

A Bit of Give and Take

'It's your fault, Eeyore,' said Rabbit.
' You've never been to see any of us. You just
stay here in this one corner of the Forest
waiting for the others to come to *you*.
Why don't you go to *them* sometimes?'

Solitude isn't Sociable

'If only,' thought Piglet, 'I had been in Pooh's house, or Christopher Robin's house, or Rabbit's house when it began to rain, then I should have had Company all this time, instead of being here all alone...'

Quality Time No. 1

Every Tuesday Roo spent
the day with his great friend
Rabbit, and Kanga
spent the day with
her great friend Pooh,

teaching him to jump,
and Piglet spent the
day with his great friend
Christopher Robin.

Say it with Flowers

Nobody had ever picked Eeyore a bunch
of violets, and the more he thought of this,
the more Piglet thought how sad it was to be
an Animal who had never had a bunch of
violets picked for him.

Appreciate What You've Got

'After all, one can't complain. I have my friends.
Somebody spoke to me only yesterday.
And was it last week or the week before that
Rabbit bumped into me and said "Bother!"
The Social Round. Always something going on.'

Quality Time No. 2

Christopher Robin and Winnie-the-Pooh
and Piglet were all talking together…

Good Deeds

Eeyore coughed in an impressive way and began to speak. 'What I did was nothing. Any of you would have done the same... I feel that we should all do what we can to help.'

Protect your Friends

So after breakfast they went round to see
Piglet and Pooh explained as they went that
Piglet was a Very Small Animal who didn't
like bouncing, and asked Tigger not to be
too Bouncy just at first.

Reward Loyalty

Christopher Robin took a stick and touched
Pooh on the shoulder, and said,
'Rise, Sir Pooh de Bear, most faithful
of all my Knights.'

Two's Company

... it was much more friendly with two.

True Friendship

'What you do *you* do, if your
house was blown down?'
'He'd come and live with me,' said Pooh,
'wouldn't you, Piglet?' Piglet squeezed his paw.
'Thank you, Pooh,' he said, 'I should love to.'

To Have a Friend is to Be One

'Oh, Bear!' said Christopher Robin.
'How I do love you!'
'So do I,' said Pooh.

A. A. Milne

A.A. Milne, born in 1882, had already made his name as a dramatist and novelist when Winnie-the-Pooh was first published in 1926. Milne's stories about Winnie-the-Pooh were written for his son, Christopher Robin. The characters in the stories were based upon the real nursery toys which belonged to Christopher Robin, and their adventures are set in Ashdown Forest where the family lived. The wise words in this little book are to be found in *Winnie-the-Pooh* and *The House at Pooh Corner*.

E. H. Shepard

E.H. Shepard became known as 'The man who drew Pooh'. Born in 1879, Shepard was able to draw well from a very young age. He won a scholarship to the Royal Academy of Arts and became an acclaimed artist and illustrator. E.H. Shepard's witty and affectionate illustrations of Pooh and his friends from the Hundred Acre Wood are an inseparable part of the appeal of the stories. His illustrations for *Winnie-the-Pooh* and *The House at Pooh Corner* have become classics, recognised all over the world.